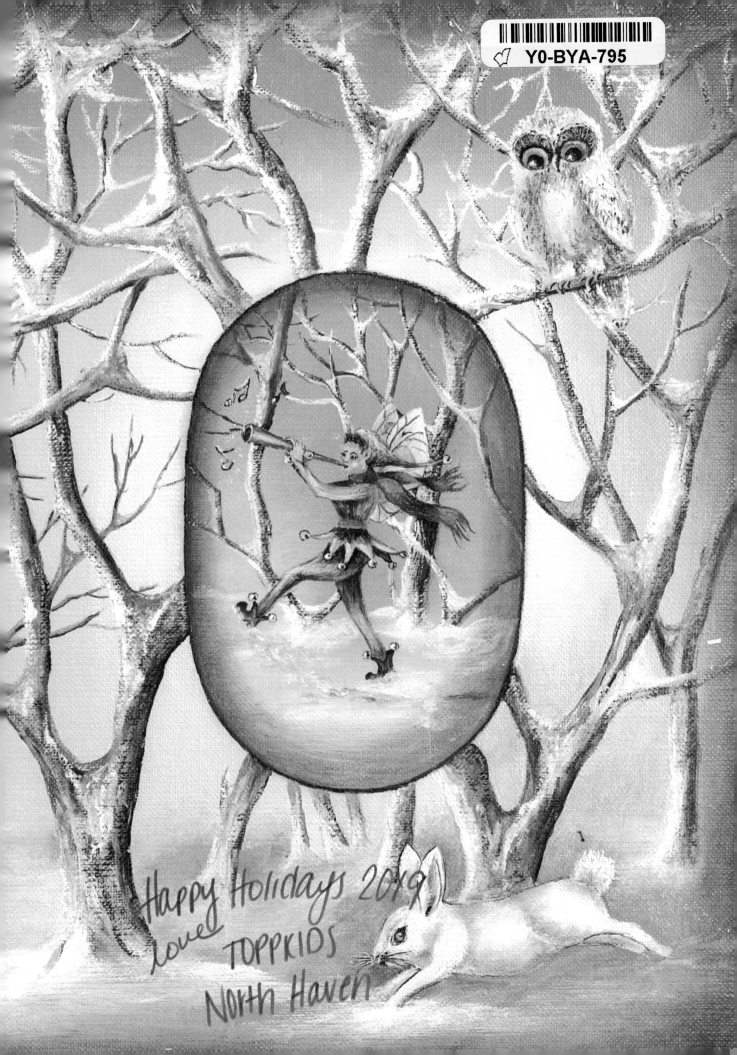

Happy Holidays 2019
Love
TOPPKIDS
North Haven

TRICKSY DEE
in
WINTER

Written and Illustrated
by
Eleanor Oltean

Foreword

There may be many who know of Eleanor Oltean as an artist who depicts, on canvas, paintings that evoke a prairie landscape. To them it may come as something of a surprise to find that she is equally at home portraying a child's world of play and fantasy. It should not surprise. Why should a landscape peopled by fairies and pixies be any less vivid or evocative than a land of prairie blizzards, pioneer cottages, or fields of golden grain? It certainly will not surprise those who have already encountered the work of this writer/illustrator in her first book about the adventures of Tricksy Dee, that endearing pixie who lives in the trunk of a tree in the heart of a forest glade and who dances the night away at the Fairy Queen Ball.

The story-in-verse that follows is a sequel to the original book; but the landscape changes. The enchanting world of leaves and flowers and grassy meadows has given way to a winter wonderland of snowflakes, snowdrifts, and snow-covered trees and hills. But Tricksy Dee has not changed. He is still the delightful creature who loves to play the same games as little girls and boys and who follows the child's imagination into a world of riding bunnies through the woods and coasting with snowflakes through the air.

In the pages that follow, little folk of all ages are welcomed into the happy winter world of Tricksy Dee.

Gustaf Kristjanson
Associate Professor of Education (retired)
University of Manitoba

Dedication

In loving memory of my beloved husband, Dean C. Oltean. Never shall I forget the joy of our fifty-eight wonderful years of marriage.

To the memory of my beloved parents, who enriched my childhood with tales of fantasy.

In loving memory of my niece Kathy. During her lifetime, we shared our love of poetry and admiration of illustrated fairy tales.

To three dear little children, all of whom I love very much: Layal, Dania, and Adam.

To all little girls and boys. I hope they will enjoy reading this book as much as I have enjoyed writing and illustrating it.

Acknowledgements

I wish to express my appreciation and sincere thanks to the following people for their support in the preparation of this book:

Professor Gustaf Kristjanson, M.A., B.A., B. Ed., for writing the foreword.

Ms. Freda Abrahamson, historian of the Leif Eriksson Club, for her contribution in writing the author biography.

To Friesens Printers for the support and excellent printing you see in this book.

To Dean Pickup of Dpict Visual Communications for the fine production of the text and illustrations, and to ABL Imaging for scanning.

To Charlene Dobmeier of Kingsley Publishing Services for managing the book project from beginning to end with confidence and competence.

I know how much you love to play
Out of doors on a winter's day.

What fun you have, when off you go,
To run and tumble in the snow.

Many things you like to do,
Pixies like to do them, too.

And Tricksy Dee is one I know,
Who loves to play in soft white snow.

E. OLTEN

Rolling snowballs on the ground,
And making them huge and round;

That is fun for pixies, too,
Just as it is fun for you.

They love to climb great drifts of snow,
And slide from peaks to valleys below.

Even a drift not so steep,
To a little pixie is a mountain peak.

But there are things that pixies do,
That little girls and boys like you

Are much too big to even try,
Like riding snowflakes in the sky!

Pixies, you know, all have wings.
They can do all sorts of things.

They can fly among the trees,
Or drift upon a gentle breeze.

They love trees covered with snow,
Sparkling white, with a magical glow,

When the moon is full and stars shine bright,
And the old owl hoots all through the night.

At times like this, Tricksy is said
To have climbed on a bunny that suddenly fled,

All through the woods at a terrible pace,
One would have thought he was running a race.

He came to a stop; he looked all around,
Then off he went with a leap and a bound.

Tricksy, I am sure, was full of fears
As he clung for his life to the bunny's ears.

There are foxes, too, in the countryside,
That will take a pixie for a lovely ride.

If it is cold and the wind blows strong,
He can cuddle in fur as he travels along.

E. OLTERN

Pixies, you know, tire of play,
Just as you do, by the end of the day.

They love the games, the laughter and fun,
But there comes a time when that is done.

Back to their homes in the woods they go.
Happy but weary they trudge through the snow.

If they feel too tired, they drift on a breeze,
To cozy homes in the trunks of the trees.

When you go out, to play in the snow
And find little tracks you don't quite know.

I can't say for sure, but it just could be
That those are the tracks of Tricksy Dee.

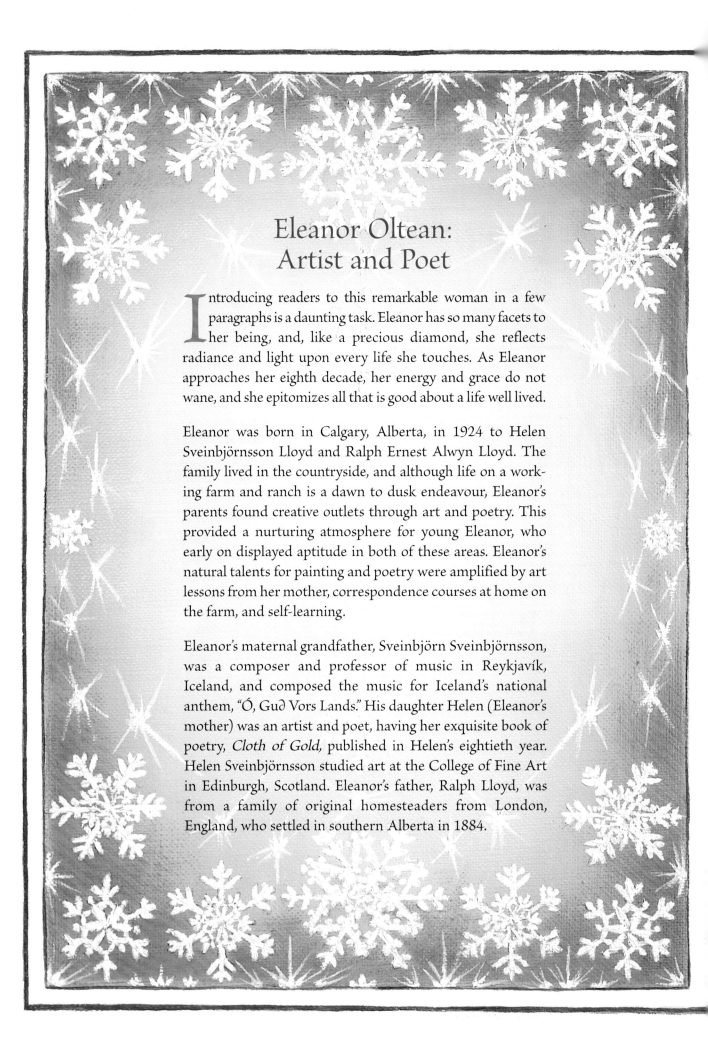

Eleanor Oltean:
Artist and Poet

Introducing readers to this remarkable woman in a few paragraphs is a daunting task. Eleanor has so many facets to her being, and, like a precious diamond, she reflects radiance and light upon every life she touches. As Eleanor approaches her eighth decade, her energy and grace do not wane, and she epitomizes all that is good about a life well lived.

Eleanor was born in Calgary, Alberta, in 1924 to Helen Sveinbjörnsson Lloyd and Ralph Ernest Alwyn Lloyd. The family lived in the countryside, and although life on a working farm and ranch is a dawn to dusk endeavour, Eleanor's parents found creative outlets through art and poetry. This provided a nurturing atmosphere for young Eleanor, who early on displayed aptitude in both of these areas. Eleanor's natural talents for painting and poetry were amplified by art lessons from her mother, correspondence courses at home on the farm, and self-learning.

Eleanor's maternal grandfather, Sveinbjörn Sveinbjörnsson, was a composer and professor of music in Reykjavík, Iceland, and composed the music for Iceland's national anthem, "Ó, Guð Vors Lands." His daughter Helen (Eleanor's mother) was an artist and poet, having her exquisite book of poetry, *Cloth of Gold,* published in Helen's eightieth year. Helen Sveinbjörnsson studied art at the College of Fine Art in Edinburgh, Scotland. Eleanor's father, Ralph Lloyd, was from a family of original homesteaders from London, England, who settled in southern Alberta in 1884.

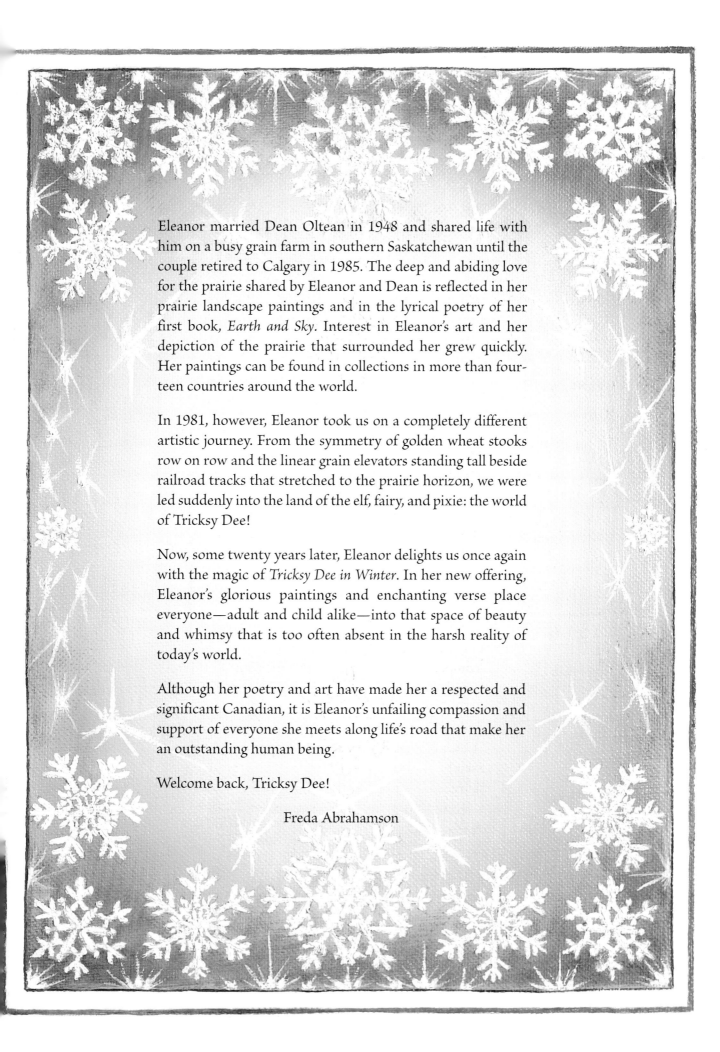

Eleanor married Dean Oltean in 1948 and shared life with him on a busy grain farm in southern Saskatchewan until the couple retired to Calgary in 1985. The deep and abiding love for the prairie shared by Eleanor and Dean is reflected in her prairie landscape paintings and in the lyrical poetry of her first book, *Earth and Sky*. Interest in Eleanor's art and her depiction of the prairie that surrounded her grew quickly. Her paintings can be found in collections in more than fourteen countries around the world.

In 1981, however, Eleanor took us on a completely different artistic journey. From the symmetry of golden wheat stooks row on row and the linear grain elevators standing tall beside railroad tracks that stretched to the prairie horizon, we were led suddenly into the land of the elf, fairy, and pixie: the world of Tricksy Dee!

Now, some twenty years later, Eleanor delights us once again with the magic of *Tricksy Dee in Winter*. In her new offering, Eleanor's glorious paintings and enchanting verse place everyone—adult and child alike—into that space of beauty and whimsy that is too often absent in the harsh reality of today's world.

Although her poetry and art have made her a respected and significant Canadian, it is Eleanor's unfailing compassion and support of everyone she meets along life's road that make her an outstanding human being.

Welcome back, Tricksy Dee!

Freda Abrahamson

Kingsley
PUBLISHING SERVICES

Project Management by Kingsley Publishing Services
Design by Dpict Visual Communications
Scanning by ABL Imaging
Printed in Canada by Friesens
1 / 2007

Library and Archives Canada Cataloguing in Publication

Oltean, Eleanor, 1924–
     Tricksy Dee in winter / written and illustrated by Eleanor Oltean.

A poem.
ISBN 978-0-9784526-0-5

     1. Children's poetry, Canadian (English). I. Title.

PS8579.L8T75 2007   jC811'.54   C2007-905497-8

Also by Eleanor Oltean